Inside...

PAGE
32
HOW TO DEFEAT SKELETONS

CUT OUT AND KEEP MINECRAFT CARDS

PAGE 37

COVERING MOBS, ITEMS, WEAPONS, VEHICLES, FOOD, ARMOUR & MORE!

Build It!

Wizard's Tower!

You're a wizard... at Minecraft! Create your own Wizard's Tower with our step-by-step guide...

1 HOUR 45 MINS

DIFFICULTY ⭐⭐⭐

HARD
THIS IS A BIG BUILD AND WILL TAKE YOU QUITE A WHILE

1

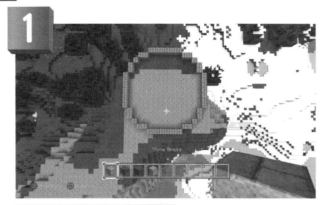

THE CIRCLE OF LIFE

▶ **BEGIN BY** building a circle block formation into the floor. The block dimensions you'll be working with here are: 7,2,1,2,7,2,1,2,7,2,1,2,7,2,1,2 If it's easier to remember, each quarter is 7 blocks, 2 right, 1 block, turn, then 2 blocks. If you repeat the last bit 4 times you'll end up with the circle all nice and, well, circular.

2

BUILD IT UP

▶ **FOR THIS** next step you'll need to go and build all the sides up by **20 blocks**. That may not seem like many blocks, but don't fret. This is only the first level of our tower. Once that's completed, head to the top and count 1 block in. What you'll be doing next is running a ring of **Stone** bricks around the inside of the top of the structure.

3

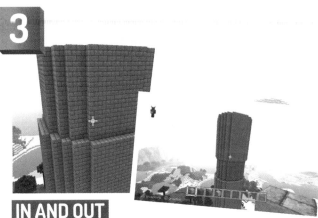

IN AND OUT

NEXT UP, build the middle section up by **10 blocks**. When you take a step back you should see a clear dip where the tower goes in. After that, run a ring around the top of the second level that's **1 block out** – so just like we did in step 1, only on top of the second section. With the new ring in, build it up by **20 more blocks**.

4

PURPLE RING... PURPLE RING

THAT'S THE main shaft of the tower now complete, so let's start working on the spire. Pull out some **Purple Concrete** and **Purple Wool**. With the **Concrete**, create a ring **1 block out** from the top of the tower. Next, create another ring **1 block in** and above. Build this ring up so it's **2 blocks higher** than the first ring.

5

TOPPING IT OFF

ON THE 2-high sections, continue building more, only this time make each one a single block in. Do this on **all 4 sides** until they meet in the middle, then fill in the corner sections. When you get to the very top, make a **2-high spike** with an ender rod on top. Lastly, use **Purple Wool** to add in lines leading into the middle as shown in the image.

6

BRANCHING OUT

HEAD TO the left side of the highest level and find the middle (this doesn't need to be exact, a rough guess will work). **1 block in** from each side, lay down **2 rows of 7 blocks**. Next, at the end of the rows, create another ring, this time with each of the main lengths being **5 blocks**, and only 2 diagonal blocks separating them.

7

HOW TALL IS YOURS?

WHERE YOU placed the 2 rows during step 6 will decide how tall your newest tower should be. Ours is **8 blocks tall**, yours may be different. The quickest way to work out how tall it should be is head to the main tower and run a line of blocks from the highest Stone bricks. Wherever the line ends above your ring is how tall this tower should be.

8

RINGS & ROWS

HEAD TO the underside of the newest tower. 1 block in, **build another ring** around the inside. When that's done, **build another row** underneath so you're left with a 2-high wall. Under that, build another ring that is, you guessed it, **1 block in**. Now go and fill in the underside so the bottom of the ring is completely flat and you can move onto step 9.

9 FENCE IT IN

ON EACH end of the flat side, on the section facing the main tower, drop down 2, 2 blocks high spikes. From here create 2 more 2 high spikes diagonally. Then 2 single blocks diagonally. And finally, 2 more 2 high spikes, this time horizontally into the building. Make each block 2 wide, and finish by adding a Fence on the second block in on each side.

10 TOPPING THE MINI-TOWER

NOW ALL that's left to do on this mini tower is the spire, which is essentially the same as the main tower's, only built with single layers instead of doubles. Run a ring around the outside, then build more single layers heading upward until all the sides meet in the middle-top. Use Purple Wool to add in our strips and this section is done!

11 AND ANOTHER ONE

REPEAT STEPS 7-10 to create a second mini-tower lower down on the front. Head to the main tower and look at it from the front. This next tower starts from the top of the bottom bit. To recap, you'll be building out, creating a ring, building the ring up, creating the underside, adding in the step formation and the fencing, then making the spire on top.

12 OPEN THE GATE

HEAD TO the bottom and smash in a 6-high, 4-wide door frame. Build the frame out of Stone so it's 3 blocks in depth. Mine up the middle row on both sides and in the section above so you're left with a gap around the inside of the frame. Fill this gap with Fences and in the centre build a 2 high Fence at the top and that's your medieval gate!

13 THE WONDER OF WINDOWS

KEEP YOUR Stone out because we'll be using it to build our windows, which also look like glyphs (magic patterns) from a distance. The trick is to build all the Glass sections 1 block back and the Stone frame 1 block out. And be sure to add the windows to all 4 sides of the towers with the exception of the sides with the walkways on.

14 DOORS MARK THE SPOT

ANOTHER NICE and easy one for you. On the walkways that lead to the mini towers add Doors at both ends. That's a total of 4 doors altogether, 2 on each walkway. These aren't essential to the build but if you ever decide to build the interior, then the doors that lead to the inside will let you know where you'll need to connect your stairs to.

15

FINISHING TOUCHES

ALL THAT'S left to do now is to create a lot of floating **fireflies** around the tower. Each one is made by placing a **Stone Slab** on the top and bottom of a block of **Glowstone**. Easy peasy. To get them all around and at different heights, just build rows of blocks coming off the main tower then place your firefly at the end before smashing up all the rows. And don't forget to set the time to night. It'll be worth it, we promise!

INSPIRATION

CASTLE FALKENSTEIN RobotChris has created an amazing medieval castle.

CASTLE ON THE MONTAIN It's astonishing what Spakstor has produced here!

BEAST'S ENCHANTED CASTLE Dennis Builds and Kellerbier's castle with rooms!

WHAT DO YOU MEAN? IT LOOKS NOTHING LIKE HOGWARTS!

DIFFICULTY

EASY
PIXEL FRUIT MODELS ARE FUN
– AND HEALTHY FOR YOU TOO!

WARNING

ASK MUM, DAD, OR WHOEVER
LOOKS AFTER YOU TO HELP WITH
KNIVES – THEY ARE SHARP!

FRUIT PIXEL SWORD!

FORGET IRON
SWORDS – FRUIT
SWORDS ARE THE
BEST!

FRUIT PIXEL SWORD

INFO

TIME NEEDED: 30 MINUTES
EXTRA INFO: MAKE IT AS
CLOSE TO THE PARTY AS
POSSIBLE, OR IT WILL GO OFF!

YOU'LL NEED...

ITEMS: Fruit! Any combination of melon, pineapple, banana, mango – basically any 4 fruits that you can chop into handy cubes to build up your sword.

1 PREPARATION

DO YOU get your five-a-day in fruit and veg? Well if you're left needing more, then a great way of bringing a fruity health kick to your next Minecraft party is with this amazing Fruit Pixel Sword! Go shopping for the kind of fruit that is quite hard to the touch – you can use any combination of fruit, whatever you like to eat. You will need 4 types for the 4 colours in the sword. One of the fruits needs to be quite dark in colour, and you will need 46 cubes of this, for the outer edge of the sword. Then 14 cubes of the blade colour, followed by 10 for the handle and 8 for the highlights. We found that different melons, mango and pineapple worked best, and banana can work, but you need to be careful not to squish it! Wash the fruit off before you start, and ask a grown up to help you remove the skin with a knife.

BE SURE TO GET
YOUR GROWN UP
HELPER TO DO ALL
THE CHOPPING!

ANY SPARE BITS
THAT AREN'T
CUBES, YOU CAN
JUST SCOFF!

2 CUBING

WITH SOLID lumps of fruit in front on you on the chopping board, turn them all into cubes (again, ask your grown up helper to help you do this with a knife – stay safe!). You want the finished cubes to be about 2x2x2cm to give a nice chunky 'pixel' for your Sword. One of the colours is only used on the handle of the Sword, so you can choose the most difficult to chop for this – so you have to chop less of it! Put each type of fruit on its own plate, so you will have a variety of colours and textures to choose from when constructing your Fruit Sword in the next stage. Any bits that aren't cube shaped – you can just scoff right now for a healthy treat!

BUILDING WITH FRUIT

TAKE A look at the template we have laid out for you here. You can see that our pixel sword is made up of 4 colours. You will need a large party platter or tray to build your sword on. We found that a plastic tray covered in tin foil worked really well – it will catch the juice that will drip out of the fruit, and also give a nice shiny surface to show off your finished sword. Be sure to save the darkest coloured fruit for the outer edge of your sword.

PIXEL PERFECT

START IN the centre of the sword design by placing the central colour line along the centre of your tray. Then build out from there, a different fruit for the main part of the sword, and one for the handle. With the main colours of your sword created, use the darker coloured fruit you selected and make the pixel outer edge that is red in our template to the right. This will give the finished sword definition.

SLICE & DICE

ONE FINISHED Fruit Pixel Sword, ready for your party guests to arrive! A finishing touch would be to add a pot of cocktail sticks next to the tray so that hungry party-goers can use these to pick out their favourite pixles to eat! If savoury is more your thing, you can always change one of the fruits for blocks of cheese instead. Cheese and pineapple go well together!

1 HOUR 45 MINUTES

FLYING HOUSE

Taking off into the sky – just like in the movie Up!

START HERE!

1 GRAB SOME Stone Bricks, Spruce Wood, a Door and build the shape shown in the picture above to act as your guideline for the house. Start with a **row of 5**. On the right, **drop 8**. Turn, then **7**. Turn again, then **5**. And finally, snake the wall back around onto itself.

2 BUILD ALL the walls up by **5 blocks** and add a **Door** in the gap. Above the door frame area, create a step effect. Here's a bonus tip: The **Skyrim mash-up pack** has some great textures for medieval buildings, but other blocks, like Wool, aren't the best to work with.

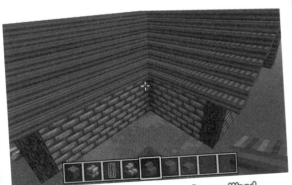

3 ARM YOURSELF with some Spruce Wood Steps. From the step effect, run Steps along the side of the larger section of the house. Continue this **up 1 level** until you have the entire larger section covered. Then, move onto the right section and do the same.

4 IN THE space in between the two sections, lay a **Stone Brick** floor. For the lamppost, lay **4** **Spruce Wood** blocks and surround the base with Steps. At the top add Glowstone. Below and above the Glowstone, run Steps. Fill the gaps with Fencing, and run Half Slabs around the middle.

5 GRAB WHITE Terracotta blocks and build a flat circle that's main length is 7 blocks long. On the back side, build everything out by 7 blocks to create a sphere shape (our football easy build covers how to do this in greater detail if you need it – it's over on page 28).

6 HEAD TO each of the flat, square shapes and knock out the corners. Then, in the natural gaps that have formed, connect the square shapes round to each other so you're left with 4 jagged spikes. On top and below, create a pyramid formation to form the balloon.

7 YOU NOW have two options for how to finish: Step 7 on its own, or Step 8 and Step 9. For the hot air balloon, pull out red Terracotta and build a shell around the upper half of the balloon. Build Fencing with Sea Lanterns coming off the longer parts, then create a pattern on the shell from Wool.

8 OR YOU can build a bunch of balloons instead. Here's how we did it: Head to the base of the sphere and with white Terracotta, create flat squares 1 block smaller than the last then knock the corners out of each of them. Lastly, run Fencing down to the house.

9 NOW TO finish, head into the second page of the Creative menu and press Down until you find the Wool sections. Fill your hotbar with different coloured wools then cover the entire sphere in all of those different wools. Don't put 2 colours together or they will stand out from a distance. Well done – you've made lots of balloons!

BUILD THIS!

LET'S SEE HOW MANY OF THOSE BALLOONS I CAN POP WITH MY ARROWS!

DIFFICULTY

HARD
THERE IS SOME TRICKY DETAIL IN THIS BUILD, BUT YOU CAN DO IT!

PUZZLES

ANSWERS ON PAGE 48

Test your brains with these teasers...

HAVE YOU GOT BLOCKS ON THE BRAIN? HOW PUZZLING!

LEAFY MAZE!

STEVE WAS chasing a **Creeper** when it darted into a leafy maze made of **Spruce Leaves**! He's a bit scared of going in by himself – can you help him through the maze of leaves to grab that pesky **Creeper**?

T	E	F
N	D	E
E	M	R

FIND THE WORD

CAN YOU work out the hidden word in this **9x9 block** of letters? It's the first word of a Minecraft item that is created by crafting a **Brown Mushroom** with **Sugar** and a **Spider Eye**. Choose a starting letter then see if you can trace your way around the block – up, down, left or right – to find the hidden word.

NAME THAT MOB

TIME TO test your knowledge of **mobs**, can you name them from a quick look at their faces? Try your luck with this trio of nasty beasties...

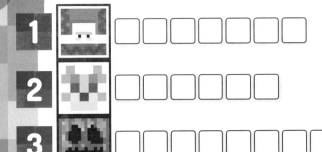

1 ☐☐☐☐☐☐☐

2 ☐☐☐☐☐☐

3 ☐☐☐☐☐☐☐☐☐☐☐☐

DOOZZZTTT! OOO... A FEEL A BIT STRANGE INSIDE!

LIGHTNING CODE

THUNDERSTORMS CAN happen at any time in the **Overworld**, and the **lightning** is responsible for turning **Pigs** into **Zombie Pigmen** and making **Creepers super charged**! This lightning bolt hides a **secret code** – follow the bolt of lightning and trace the pattern on the letter block to discover what it says!

B	T	E	L	C
A	S	H	N	E
T	T	E	S	T
E	P	H	E	N
I	C	K	R	N
O	B	E	D	R
T	R	S	W	A
D	S	E	R	E
M	R	I	C	R
R	A	F	T	Y
H	E	G	O	M
M	I	G	H	N
T	C	S	I	Y
H	D	O	G	L
O	A	R	T	T
I	E	C	G	A
G	N	I	T	N

HOW TO SURVIVE IN THE NETHER

Too scared to go into The Nether? Not with our tips!

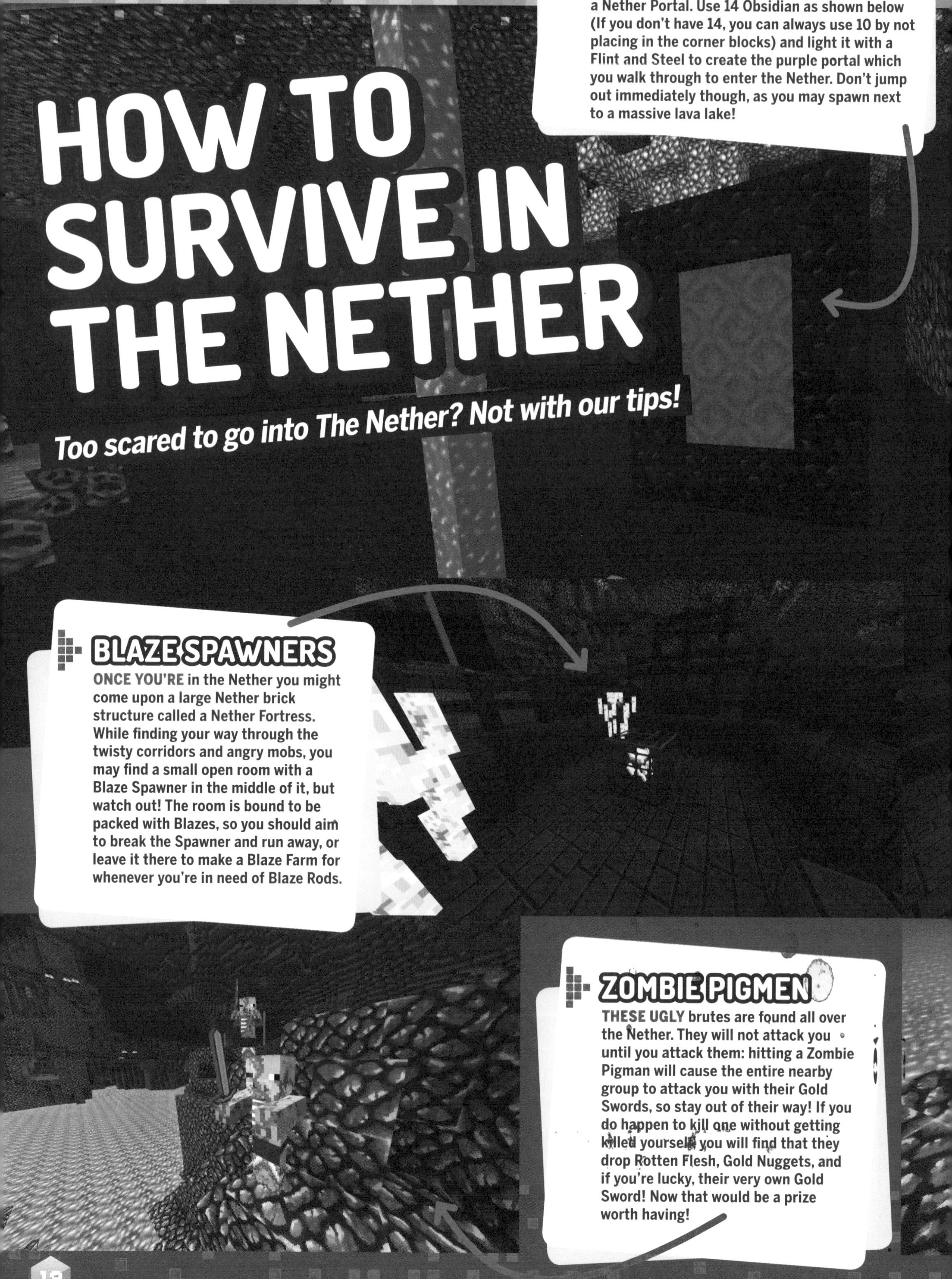

NETHER PORTALS

BEFORE EXPLORING the Nether you need to build a Nether Portal. Use 14 Obsidian as shown below (If you don't have 14, you can always use 10 by not placing in the corner blocks) and light it with a Flint and Steel to create the purple portal which you walk through to enter the Nether. Don't jump out immediately though, as you may spawn next to a massive lava lake!

BLAZE SPAWNERS

ONCE YOU'RE in the Nether you might come upon a large Nether brick structure called a Nether Fortress. While finding your way through the twisty corridors and angry mobs, you may find a small open room with a Blaze Spawner in the middle of it, but watch out! The room is bound to be packed with Blazes, so you should aim to break the Spawner and run away, or leave it there to make a Blaze Farm for whenever you're in need of Blaze Rods.

ZOMBIE PIGMEN

THESE UGLY brutes are found all over the Nether. They will not attack you until you attack them: hitting a Zombie Pigman will cause the entire nearby group to attack you with their Gold Swords, so stay out of their way! If you do happen to kill one without getting killed yourself you will find that they drop Rotten Flesh, Gold Nuggets, and if you're lucky, their very own Gold Sword! Now that would be a prize worth having!

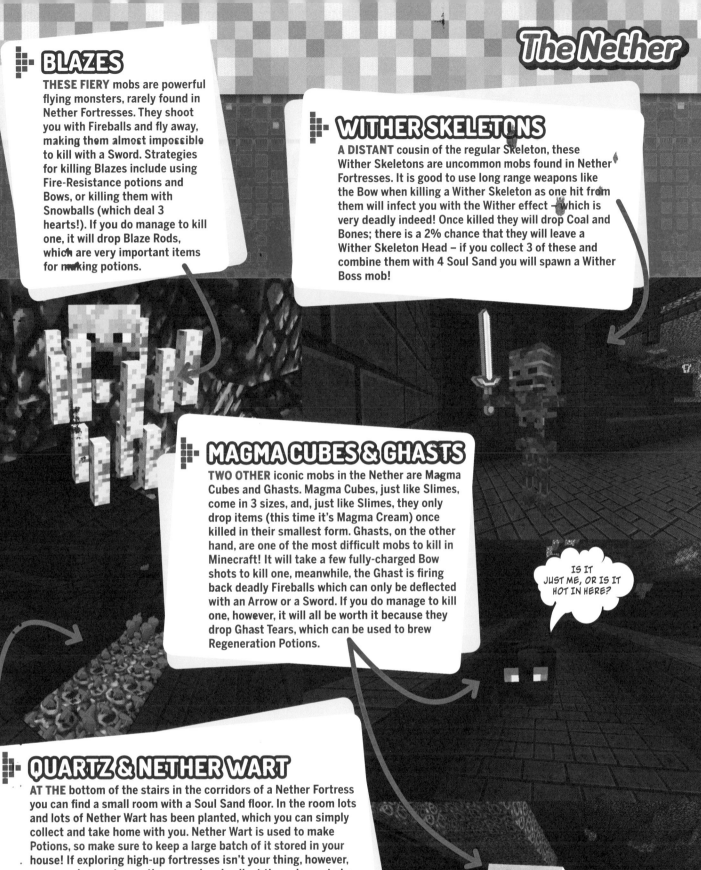

BLAZES

THESE FIERY mobs are powerful flying monsters, rarely found in Nether Fortresses. They shoot you with Fireballs and fly away, making them almost impossible to kill with a Sword. Strategies for killing Blazes include using Fire-Resistance potions and Bows, or killing them with Snowballs (which deal 3 hearts!). If you do manage to kill one, it will drop Blaze Rods, which are very important items for making potions.

WITHER SKELETONS

A DISTANT cousin of the regular Skeleton, these Wither Skeletons are uncommon mobs found in Nether Fortresses. It is good to use long range weapons like the Bow when killing a Wither Skeleton as one hit from them will infect you with the Wither effect – which is very deadly indeed! Once killed they will drop Coal and Bones; there is a 2% chance that they will leave a Wither Skeleton Head – if you collect 3 of these and combine them with 4 Soul Sand you will spawn a Wither Boss mob!

MAGMA CUBES & GHASTS

TWO OTHER iconic mobs in the Nether are Magma Cubes and Ghasts. Magma Cubes, just like Slimes, come in 3 sizes, and, just like Slimes, they only drop items (this time it's Magma Cream) once killed in their smallest form. Ghasts, on the other hand, are one of the most difficult mobs to kill in Minecraft! It will take a few fully-charged Bow shots to kill one, meanwhile, the Ghast is firing back deadly Fireballs which can only be deflected with an Arrow or a Sword. If you do manage to kill one, however, it will all be worth it because they drop Ghast Tears, which can be used to brew Regeneration Potions.

IS IT JUST ME, OR IS IT HOT IN HERE?

QUARTZ & NETHER WART

AT THE bottom of the stairs in the corridors of a Nether Fortress you can find a small room with a Soul Sand floor. In the room lots and lots of Nether Wart has been planted, which you can simply collect and take home with you. Nether Wart is used to make Potions, so make sure to keep a large batch of it stored in your house! If exploring high-up fortresses isn't your thing, however, you can always stay on the ground and collect the only ore to be found in the Nether, Quartz. Quartz is found in huge veins all across the Nether, so you will almost never run out of it! It can be used to make Quartz blocks, but even if you don't want the blocks, mining the ore itself gives you a lot of experience points.

60 MINUTES!

WHAT DO YOU MEAN I LOOK LIKE SOMETHING DRINKING IN THE SPACE CANTINA?

STAR WARS AT-ST

One for fans of stuff that happened long, long ago...

DIFFICULTY

EASY
USE THE FORCE TO HELP YOU WITH THIS EASY BUILD!

START HERE!

1 START BY building the foot on the right, which is a mix of 4, 3, and 5-long rows built inwards. From there, build 3 2x2 cuboids heading up, the flat panel, then a 3D rectangle on top. Build out the arm, then add in the 9-wide black section. And then do it all over again to create the other leg!

2 FOR THIS next part we'll be building the base shell of the head. On both of the arms, add in the square sections. Run Grey Wool across the middle, then add in the Light Grey Wool wall. Now repeat that last part again on the opposite side before creating the front cannons from Black Wool.

3 NOW IT'S just a case of building up the sections from the last step and adding in some detail. Build around the gun then add a wall heading vertically. Behind the front wall, add a larger wall, and its sides, and add the eye holes at the top, then the mini-guns on either side.

BUILD THIS!

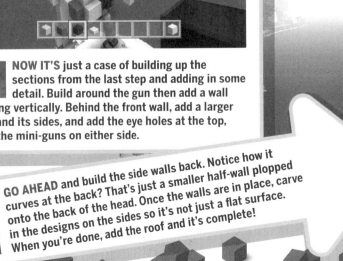

4 GO AHEAD and build the side walls back. Notice how it curves at the back? That's just a smaller half-wall plopped onto the back of the head. Once the walls are in place, carve in the designs on the sides so it's not just a flat surface. When you're done, add the roof and it's complete!

KNOW YOUR BIOMES
TAIGA

YOU WILL FIND the Taiga biomes covered in a forest of Spruce trees, so they are a great place for stocking up on wood for your builds. Flowers and giant ferns also grow well here. Villages can generate in the Taiga, with the houses using the Spruce wood as their main building block.

WATCH OUT FOR WILD WOLVES IN THE TAIGA, THEY ROAM AROUND THE FORESTS LOOKING FOR RABBITS TO EAT. THEY WON'T ATTACK YOU THOUGH, IN FACT YOU CAN TAME THEM.

RABBITS, RABBITS... EVERYWHERE! THE FAVOURITE SNACK OF THE WOLF, YOU CAN FIND BLACK, BROWN AND GREY RABBITS AROUND THESE PARTS. THEY ARE COMPLETELY HARMLESS, AND GREAT FOR FOOD!

DIFFICULTY

EASY
WHO DOESN'T LOVE A BIT OF JUNK MODELLING?

TOILET ROLL CREEPER!

Brighten up your game den (or bedroom) with this cool Creeper – made from toilet rolls and a box!

TOILET ROLL CREEPER

INFO

TIME NEEDED: 60 MINUTES
EXTRA INFO: MOST OF THAT TIME IS WAITING FOR THE PAINT AND GLUE TO DRY!

YOU'LL NEED...

ITEMS: 3 toilet rolls (the used tubes, without the paper), a small box, green paint (or blue and yellow to make green), coloured paper (green, black and grey), glue, a black marker pen.

1 TAKING THE TUBE

THE LAST thing you want to hear when you're 'using' toilet rolls is the hiss of a Creeper, but next time be sure to save the toilet roll tubes as we're making a cool Creeper model out of cardboard tubes and boxes! Gather all of your bits together on a tray, then start by taking **3 toilet roll tubes** and cutting **2 slits about 2cm in length** into 2 of them, about **3cm apart**. Slot the third toilet roll into the slits

YOU CAN ADJUST THE LENGTH OF THE SLITS YOU CUT TO CHANGE THE HEIGHT OF YOUR FINISHED CREEPER!

WARNING

ASK MUM, DAD, OR WHOEVER LOOKS AFTER YOU TO HELP WITH SCISSORS – THEY ARE SHARP!

2 BOXING CLEVER

CUT THE small box down to size and stick the ends so that it doesn't come apart. You want to end up with something **block shaped** (well this is Minecraft after all)! We used an old medicine box as it was larger than toothpaste boxes – you want your Creeper's head to be a good size. Add some glue to the bottom of the box and **stick it to the top toilet roll tube** to form the head. You can adjust the length of the slits in your tubes to create a Creeper of the height you would like for your model.

GLUE FOR STRENGTH

WITH THE size of your Creeper decided, add some dabs of glue to the insides of the slits to give your model some strength. Now you need to put it aside for the glue to dry.

LET THE GLUE DRY BEFORE PAINTING

CREEPER GREEN

TIME TO open up the paint – cover your model with a nice bright green paint as close to a Creeper colour as you can mix. If you don't have any green paint then you can easily mix the right colour using blue and yellow. If your green is a bit too dark, add a bit more yellow and mix it well. Once painted put the Creeper to one side again for the paint to completely dry, ready for the next stage.

IF YOU HAVE GREEN PAINT – GREAT! IF NOT, YOU CAN GET THE RIGHT COLOUR BY MIXING BLUE AND YELLOW TOGETHER

PIECES OF PIXEL

TIME TO give your Creeper some detail now! You can either use black craft paper for his eyes and mouth, or use a black marker pen to draw the black details on – you know what a Creeper's face looks like, but if you need reminding, we've included the face here for you to copy. You now need a few colours of other craft paper, or any kind of coloured paper will work. Green, silver, black, grey – they will all work well for a Creeper. Cut the paper into various sizes of square then glue them all around the model to give your Creeper a pixel effect. Alternatively, stick the paper on while the paint is still wet – no need for glue!

ERR... CAN SOMEONE PAINT A FACE ON ME PLEASE!

GIVE THE CREEPER A PIXEL EFFECT WITH PAPER SQUARES

HISSSSS...

AND THERE you have it! A scary Creeper model that can sit on the TV or computer screen and watch you playing Minecraft. Why not make two or three and create a display of them with other Minecraft blocks?

DIFFICULTY

NORMAL
THE FARM AND BARN LOOK
GREAT, BUT ARE NOT TRICKY

BUILD A SURVIVAL FARM

60 MINUTES!

INFO

SURVIVAL FARM

TIME NEEDED: 1 HOUR
EXTRA INFO: YOU CAN MIX UP
THE INSTRUCTIONS TO MAKE
THE FARM TO SUIT YOUR WORLD

Tackling Survival Mode can be made easier with a well stocked farm. Let us show you how to build one...

I'M MOOOOVING IN TO THIS AMAZING FARM!

PLANNING THE BARN

1 TO KICK things off we need to build the floorplan for our large farm barn. Grab some Spruce Logs and drop 4 down with 2 blocks of space in-between. Add 2 more rows, again 2 blocks apart, north of the previous row. Then on the far right, count 4 blocks out and place a row of 3 blocks, 2 apart. Build the Wood up by 4 blocks except for the middle-left 3, which are only 3 blocks high. To finish, fill in the left, right and top sides with 3 high Stone blocks

RAISE THE ROOF

2 **NEXT WE'RE** going to build the base of our roof. Grab your **Spruce Logs** once more and fill in the left and right sides. From here, run a line across the middle, going directly on top of the shorter pillars we laid down in the last step. Run **2 more rows** on the north and south sides, then finish up by running **3 more smaller rows** from south to north and you're done.

I'D LIKE A GOLD PIGSTY WITH HOT AND COLD SLOP, PLEASE!

WALKING THE PLANK

3 **ADD SPRUCE** **Planks** and **Wooden Fence** to your hotbar. Ignoring the large gap to the right, run the **Spruce Planks** along the ground from left to right. When you reach the large gap, turn and enter the structure and drop some more **Planks** as well as a gate for easy access. Now place **Fences** on top of the Planks to make sure any horses you wrangle don't escape and run amok.

UP ON THE ROOF

4 **UP NEXT**, the roof of our stable. For this, head back to the top with your **Spruce Planks** and wherever you see the white side of the **Spruce Logs**, place a Plank. Then create a step effect by building **1 block out**, laying a block on top, then deleting the corner of the 'L' shape. Do this on both sides until you eventually meet the natural middle, which will end up being the main strip of the roof.

SPRUCE IT UP

5 **YOUR ROOF** won't look much like a roof at this point, but that's okay. Here's a tip to make a roof less dull. Grab some steps, **Spruce Steps** to be exact. In-between each of the Planks lay down steps and connect them to the next Plank along. Repeat this process until all the gaps are covered in steps then run **Half Slabs** round the bottom and fill in the west and east sides with **Spruce** to finish your lovely roof.

Build It!

BUILDING THE BARN

6 WITH YOUR stable finished find a large plot of land nearby for your barn. Ours is to the right of the stable, but feel free to change this as you see fit. Next, with **Spruce Logs**, drop down a row of **5 blocks**, count **5 blocks** to the right and add in another row of **5 Spruce Logs**. On each row build the sides up by 5 then place a **3x3 wall of Stone** blocks in the middle. Round it out by placing a row of **Spruce Logs** on top.

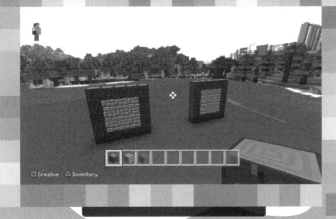

PUT UP A SPIKE

8 BUILD A **5 high spike** on top of the centre of the arch. To the left and right of the spike, put **2 more sets of Planks** in a step formation. When that's completed, grab your trusty **Spruce Logs** and while looking down, place blocks on top of the Plank steps. If you've done this correctly you shouldn't need to place a middle block in the top-centre as it'll already be there.

MAKING THE WALLS

9 FOR THE walls, build from the **back of the barn to the front**. Ensure the Wood is all facing the same way, build it from ground level upwards (laying them down from left to right means the wall will take on a different shape thanks to the way Wood placement works). Build walls on both sides and be sure to extend them by **12 blocks**. Don't worry about the solid wood look as we'll be sprucing (get the joke?!) it up later.

ONE BIG LOG

7 ON EACH of the corners and the tops add a single **Spruce Log** to help create the effect it's all one big long log that's been lowered into place. Head to the middle and on the left and right **build up by 3** and connect the **2 spikes** to create an entrance arch. Add some more **single blocks** for the log effect and end by placing **Spruce Planks** in a step formation on each side.

AND REPEAT

10 FOR THIS next part we're going to need to rebuild the front side once more, only on the opposite end. You can either head back to **step 6** for instructions or if you're up for a challenge, create the back by copying the front from memory! The general rule here is lay down **Spruce Logs** as your guideline then add in the **Stone Bricks** and step **Planks** afterwards.

SPRUCE STEPS

11 NEXT WE'LL be putting what we learned from step 5 back into action again. Pick a wall, then count **2 blocks in from the left** and drop in a **Spruce Log** facing up. Count another **2 blocks** along and drop down **2 Spruce Logs** next to one another. Count **2 blocks** again then drop another one down. Now create a step effect heading into the middle out of **Spruce Logs** to create the frame of our roof.

STONE SIDES

12 FOR THIS next part, fill in all the spaces, from left to right, between the Spruce frame with **Spruce Steps**. Once that's done, your barn roof should be fully completed, so now we'll tackle the sides of the barn. If you're after something quick and simple, grab some **Stone** then mine up **4 rows** and the centre piece before filling them in with **Stone**.

HOMES FOR ANIMALS

13 FOR THE inside of the barn, connect the two sections parallel with the front where the logs stick out. Count **3 blocks** along and build a **Spruce pillar**, then **4 blocks** and another pillar, then **3**. In the gaps lay down **Spruce Planks** with **Fences** on top of them to create **3 animal pens**. Mirror this on the opposite side, then you can add **Torches** to make sure you don't get any uninvited guests during the night.

WHAT KIND OF TIE WOULD A PIG WEAR?

A PIGS-TIE OF COURSE!

YOUR 5 A DAY

14 WHAT'S A farm without a decent supply of crops for your adventuring? To finish this build, build six **5x5** plots and dig up a **1 block moat** around all of them. Grab yourself a **Water Bucket** and fill the moat; this will help your crops grow much more quickly. Add fencing around the entire area. Gates to get in and out, and a single block of **Grass** between each section for access. Now that's this build finished, you can now go out and find yourself as many animals as you can. After all, you've got an entire farm to fill!

KNOW YOUR BIOMES
EXTREME HILLS

WITH MOUNTAINS SOARING high into the sky, the Extreme Hills biome is covered in Oak and Spruce trees to mine. You can often find a great view from these hills, with waterfalls, caverns, valleys and even floating islands – Avatar style – to discover.

THE MONSTER EGG BLOCK IS FOUND IN THE EXTREME HILLS. IT MIGHT LOOK LIKE A STANDARD STONE BLOCK, BUT ON SMASHING IT YOU WILL UNLEASH A SILVERFISH! IF A BLOCK SEEMS TO BE TAKING TOO LONG TO BREAK – RUN AWAY!

THE EXTREME HILLS ARE ONE OF THE FEW PLACES THAT LLAMAS AND SILVERFISH SPAWN NATURALLY! WHILE LLAMAS ARE FRIENDLY, WATCH OUT FOR THOSE NASTY SILVERFISH!

ANCIENT TEMPLE

A place for scary skeletons to roam!

START HERE!

1 **START BY** finding a **large, flat area** in your world big enough for a temple! Fill your hotbar with **End Stone** blocks. The outermost wall of our ancient temple is **20x20** blocks, **2 blocks high**, but leave gaps in the centre of each wall as a way in that we will fill in with steps later on.

2 **NOW IT'S** time to build those staggered walls up high. Follow the pattern – **up 3 blocks, in 3 blocks, up 3 blocks, in 3 blocks** – just like in the picture above. Do this all the way around the temple, then build a higher wall **6 blocks high** all the way around on top, giving the 4 sides a doorway.

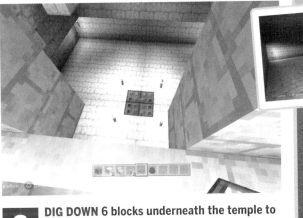

3 **DIG DOWN 6** blocks underneath the temple to create a **secret burial chamber**, with a floor of **End Stone**. You can light the walls with **Torches**. Now at entrance level, do a second floor of **End Stone** with a **2x2** entrance in the centre made from **Wooden Trap Doors**. Put 4 Torches around the Trap Door.

4 **BUILD STAIRCASES** up the 4 sides of the temple with **Sandstone Stairs** to finish off. Then fill in the top of the roof to block out the light. On discovering your temple people will be curious and walk up the sides – the view greeting them will be your trap door to something scary! Dare they enter the **secret burial chamber**?

BUILD THIS!

23

TOP 10 SCARY MOBS!

We count down the mobs that make us run!

> WHAT DO YOU MEAN I ONLY MADE NUMBER 11! GRRRR...

1 CREEPER

ALTHOUGH THEY are scary hostile mobs that are out to get you, we can't help loving the Creepers! They have become the symbol of Minecraft, and we bet you've got a few things in your bedroom with Creepers on! Me? I'm sitting on a Creeper cushion as I write this!

CREEPERS WILL give chase if you come within 16 blocks of them, or, if you are wearing a Creeper mob head they will chase you at 8 blocks when they realise you're not one of them! They can climb up vines and ladders, so don't think you can climb your way to safety!

HOW DO they attack you? Well once you're within 3 blocks of them they start their scary hiss and inflate themselves! After just 1.5 seconds of this, they will explode, taking you and anything else in the area with them. You can stop this by moving away pretty quickly.

> IT'SSSSSS SSSSSSO NICE TO BE IN A MINECRAFT BOOK!

THERE'S A special kind of Creeper that is created when Lightning strikes a regular one – the Charged Creeper! One of these has massively increased explosive powers and will take out an entire village if it is set off! Any Zombies, Wither Skeletons or regular Skeletons caught in the blast will drop their heads.

THEY MIGHT be scary when bumped into on a dark night, but did you know that Creepers are scared of cats? It's true! If they come across an Ocelot they will run away from it at twice the speed that they run at you! Maybe it's because they look like they're made of leaves, and a cat would want to scratch it?!

2 SPIDERS

THE FACT that these things are the only mobs in Minecraft that can climb walls is the most terrifying thing! Just when you think you're safe, they will leap out of nowhere and nab you! Try shooting them from a distance with Arrows and if shot they will give chase in the direction the arrow came from! Here's an extra scary thought – if you use a splash potion of Invisibility on them, their bodies disappear but their red beady eyes remain staring at you! Aarrggghh!

3 ZOMBIE

THERE ARE lots of different kinds of Zombies in Minecraft, they are undead mobs that can come in grown up and baby versions. Take extra care if you find yourself in a village with over 10 doors and 20 Villagers at midnight – this is when 20 Zombies can spawn on the outskirts of the village and attack! When Mojang first promoted Zombies coming to Minecraft they did it with a poster that said, "Zombie Infection! The disease is spreading! "Uuuuhh, ooohhh"!

4 GHAST

SHOOTING FIREBALLS from their mouths, Ghasts are a nasty mob found in The Nether. They go around with their eyes and mouth shut making weird cat-like noises, until they see you, then they let rip with blasts of fireballs and scream at you! At close range, the Ghast's fireballs are about the most powerful mob attack found in the game – so don't get at close range to them!

5 WITHER

THIS THREE-HEADED boss mob is simply mad! When spawned it fires Wither Skulls out from its three heads and inflicts a creeping corruption on you that will turn your hearts black! Not only is it out to destory every living thing around it, the Wither will also destroy any blocks it comes into contact with, so even if you survive an attack, there will be nothing much left of your world!

6

ZOMBIE PIGMAN

COMING IN both adult and baby forms, the Zombie Pigman is formed when a Pig gets struck by lightning. They carry Golden Swords and have a half-Pig/half-Zombie face. They are quite slow, so easily outrun, but they will keep on coming for you, knocking on the door if you hide inside a house! Watch out if you attack one – every other Zombie Pigman around will centre in on you and come to its aid. You don't want an army of them around you!

7

SKELETON HORSE

AWWW... WHO doesn't love horses, eh? Which makes it all the more terrifying when you see them turned into skeletons! Minecraft has something called the 'Skeleton Trap'. It happens when lightning strikes a horse – it transforms it into a Skeleton Horse, with a Skeleton rider on its back. This will then spawn three more of these abominations, they will strafe around you and attack. Each Skeleton has an Enchanted Bow and Enchanted Iron Helmet. Poor horse.

8

CHICKEN JOCKEY

NOW THESE things are super-rare! If a Baby Zombie, Baby Husk, Baby Zombie Villager or Baby Zombie Pigman spawn within a 10 block radius of a Chicken, it will appear riding the Chicken and make a Chicken Jockey! They run around just like the mob on their back, except in Pocket Edition where they act like Chickens!

9

ENDERMAN

THESE TALL, thin, black mobs don't like being stared at! All you've got to do is look in their direction a bit too long and they will come after you – teleporting around The End, picking up random blocks and attacking you. Luckily they are also easily distracted, so if another mob gets in the way, or even if it starts to rain, they will forget all about you and continue with their lives. Phew!

10

ENDER DRAGON

HE'S THE grandaddy of all the mobs in Minecraft – the Ender Dragon was the very first boss mob to be put into the game. When you enter The End, the dragon spawns and starts to circle around. Any block it hits, it will destroy, unless they are special The End blocks like Obsidian and End Stone. It has Ender Charges, purple fireballs that it will shoot at you.

KNOW YOUR BIOMES
BEACH

WE ALL LOVE a trip to the beach! As you would expect, mining at the Beach you can find Sand, Gravel and Water blocks. As you would not expect, you can also get Sugar Cane blocks at the beach too! A Beach biome appears wherever the Ocean meets other biomes, the Sand blocks covering up the usual blocks of that biome.

JUST LIKE IN REAL LIFE, BEACHES CAN FORM IN VARIOUS WAYS. SOME HAVE IN-LAND PONDS, OTHERS CREATE PENINSULAS WITH A LONG AREA OF SAND REACHING OUT INTO THE OCEAN. THE ONE THING THE BEACH IS USEFUL FOR IS FISHING.

THERE'S NOT A LOT OF LIFE TO BE FOUND ON THE BEACH IN MINECRAFT. PASSIVE MOBS DON'T SPAWN HERE AT ALL.

30 MINUTES!

I'M FOOTBALL CRAZY... FOOTBALL MAD!

A FOOTBALL!

Master building a sphere in Minecraft!

START HERE!

1 ROUND THINGS made out of blocks can be tricky. Start by creating a flat, vertical circle. Run a row of 5 white Wool blocks then for the corners, run 2 blocks horizontally, 1 block, then 2 blocks vertically. Connect the corners back onto a second run of 5. Repeat this pattern until you've got an outline, then fill in the middle.

2 NEXT UP, find the centre and create a 5x5 square then build it out by 5 blocks. On top, count 1 block back and drop in a 2 high vertical row. Then another row on top of that. And finish with 2 wide flat section. Do the same on the underside as well.

3 HEAD BEHIND the circle and build all the walls out by 5 blocks. From here, you should be able to repeat Step 2 on the bottom, top, and opposite side of your football. Fill in the walls once more and you should be left with a weird 'plus' shape when viewed from above.

BUILD THIS!

4 ON EVERY 5x5 face shape, knock out the corners. Then parallel with them, fill in the gap between each of the 4 sections you just built. Above and below each of the 4 new walls, create pyramids. To turn the sphere into a football, change the sphere face shapes and pyramids to black Wool!

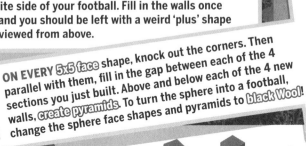

PUZZLES

Test your brains with these teasers...

IF YOU FIND ONE PROBLEM TOO HARD, TRY AN UDDER ONE!

ANSWERS ON PAGE 48

TRACKBLOCK

THIS BLOCK hides three 9 letter words connected to our favourite videogame! Can you find them all?

T F A
I N R
M E C
O P H E
R B S L
T F O K F
L E O
O W

HIDDEN BLOCKS

THIS WORD BLOCK has the names of four different types of block frozen inside it – can you draw a line from letter to letter to find out which types are hiding in there?

G N E X
O R M X
L G A I
M E L S
M A S X

SPOT THE DIFFERENCE

HOW MANY differences do you think there are between these two pictures from Minecraft: Story Mode? It's more tricky than you may think! Write your number below.

PICTURE 1

PICTURE 2

WRITE IN HOW MANY YOU THINK!

20 MINUTES!

BUNK BEDS!

Have yourself the perfect sleepover with these...

BAGSY I'M GETTING THE TOP BUNK FOR OUR MINECRAFT SLEEPOVER!

DIFFICULTY

NORMAL
NOTHING TOO TRICKY HERE, BUT GREAT FOR SLEEPOVERS!

START HERE!

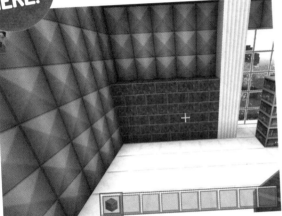

1 LET'S KICKSTART this bunk bed build by creating a 3 high wall that's 5 blocks across out of Black Wool. This smaller section is going to act as the back of our bunk beds. Feel free to place it wherever you want, but for the sake of simplicity, we placed it in the corner of a room.

2 WITH THE back side of your beds laid down we can now start work on one of the sides. Looking directly at the front of the wall you just built, aim your eyes to the left and extend the wall so that it comes out by 2 blocks, again making this from Black Wool.

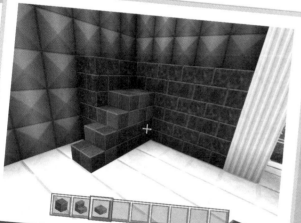

3 TO THE right of the jutting out section, drop down 2 more Wool blocks coming from the back wall. After that, place 1 single block of Purpur on top of the furthest back block, then add in some Purpur steps in front of the Purpur block and in front of the Wool blocks.

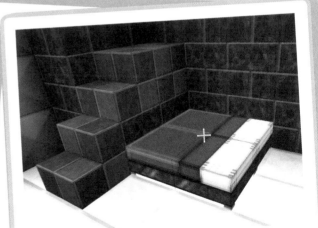

4 NEXT GRAB some Beds and stand on top of the Purpur blocks. Look to the right and lay down 2 Beds next to one another on the ground. Make sure that the pillow area is 2 blocks away from you so whoever sleeps in the top bunk doesn't accidentally step on your head.

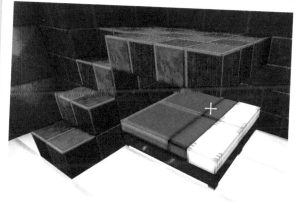

5 NOW WE'RE going to need to make a giant slab to hold the top bunk bed in place. Grab some Purpur Half Slabs and connect them to the single Purpur block and the set of steps next to it. This should look like a mini small roof over the 2 Beds. This will carry the next Beds in our project.

6 YOUR BUNK beds should now be starting to take shape, so let's add 2 more Beds on top of the Purpur Half Slabs. As with the last beds, it's best to keep them facing the same way to mirror the bottom bunk and, again, to avoid any accidental head-smushing.

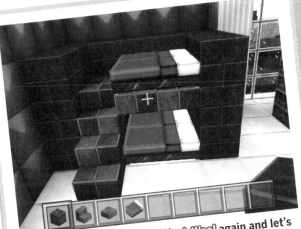

7 GRAB YOUR trusty Black Wool again and let's finish off the sides of the bunks. Look to where the back Black Wool pokes out to right of the beds. From here, build another 3 High wall. Basically, we're repeating what we did in step 2, only on the furthest right hand side.

8 NOW FOR some finishing decorations. Head into the menu and grab some Purpur Half Slabs. See how the Black Wool creates a kind of 'C' shape around the bunks? Simply run a row of slabs around the top of the bunks. Doing so definitely helps to break up all the black.

BUILD THIS!

I WARN YOU... I SNORE IN BED!

9 TO FINISH up this build we're going to add some drawers to the bunks. To do this, place 2 Item Frames on both sides of the bottom bunk. Then all that's left is to fill them with Wooden Buttons and they should end up looking like drawers full of toys. Now you can jump into bed!

HOW TO DEFEAT SKELETONS

Our Minecraft Experts show you the best way...

NO RUNNING

NEVER RUN directly at a Skeleton unless you want to die incredibly fast. Instead, try your best to zig-zag towards them. Running either left-and-forwards or right-and-forwards means the arrows will be shot at where you were, rather than where you are, making survival much more likely.

WHACKING TIME!

WHENEVER YOU'RE in a cave, chances are you've got a selection of random blocks, probably Dirt or Cobblestone. When you eventually do come across a Skeleton, build yourself a 2 high, 3 wide wall and hide behind the middle. The Skeleton will eventually come and find you, and when it does, it'll now be within whacking distance.

CREEPER POWER

HOW MANY times has a Creeper ended your run? Now it's time to turn the tables! If you ever see a Skeleton within the same area as a Creeper, ignore the Skeleton and aggro the Creeper. Make the Creeper follow you so it's near the Skeleton, and when it starts flashing, run off giggling as it blows up itself and the Skeleton.

READY... FIGHT!

SKELETONS NORMALLY have the upper hand in a fight. But if you see it first, you can win with some clever thinking. When spotted, mine up so you're above it but not so high you'll take fall damage. Line it up, then divebomb onto the Skeleton while swinging your sword. They'll never know what hit them.

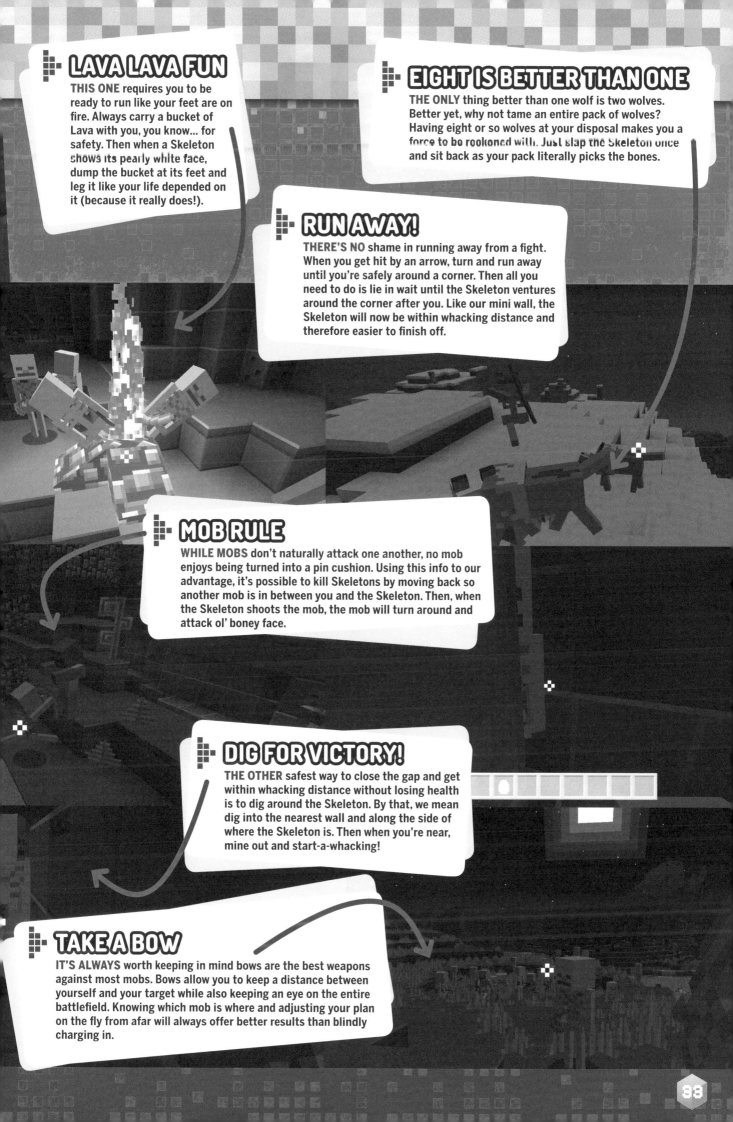

LAVA LAVA FUN

THIS ONE requires you to be ready to run like your feet are on fire. Always carry a bucket of Lava with you, you know... for safety. Then when a Skeleton shows its pearly white face, dump the bucket at its feet and leg it like your life depended on it (because it really does!).

EIGHT IS BETTER THAN ONE

THE ONLY thing better than one wolf is two wolves. Better yet, why not tame an entire pack of wolves? Having eight or so wolves at your disposal makes you a force to be reckoned with. Just slap the Skeleton once and sit back as your pack literally picks the bones.

RUN AWAY!

THERE'S NO shame in running away from a fight. When you get hit by an arrow, turn and run away until you're safely around a corner. Then all you need to do is lie in wait until the Skeleton ventures around the corner after you. Like our mini wall, the Skeleton will now be within whacking distance and therefore easier to finish off.

MOB RULE

WHILE MOBS don't naturally attack one another, no mob enjoys being turned into a pin cushion. Using this info to our advantage, it's possible to kill Skeletons by moving back so another mob is in between you and the Skeleton. Then, when the Skeleton shoots the mob, the mob will turn around and attack ol' boney face.

DIG FOR VICTORY!

THE OTHER safest way to close the gap and get within whacking distance without losing health is to dig around the Skeleton. By that, we mean dig into the nearest wall and along the side of where the Skeleton is. Then when you're near, mine out and start-a-whacking!

TAKE A BOW

IT'S ALWAYS worth keeping in mind bows are the best weapons against most mobs. Bows allow you to keep a distance between yourself and your target while also keeping an eye on the entire battlefield. Knowing which mob is where and adjusting your plan on the fly from afar will always offer better results than blindly charging in.

PUZZLES

Test your brains with these teasers...

NAME THAT MOB

HOW WELL do you know your Minecraft mobs? Whether they are chasing after you making hissing noises, or swapping Emeralds for bread, can you **identify these mobs by their face** alone?

A NICE EASY ONE TO START YOU OFF!

1
2
3
4
5
6
7

ANSWERS ON PAGE 48

FOOD SUDOKU

HAVE YOU tried a Sudoku? It's a tricky puzzle where you must make sure that **each line of 4**, top to bottom and left to right, **has only one of each item**. Oh, and each block of 4 also has to have only one of each item too. See if you can **draw in the missing food**...

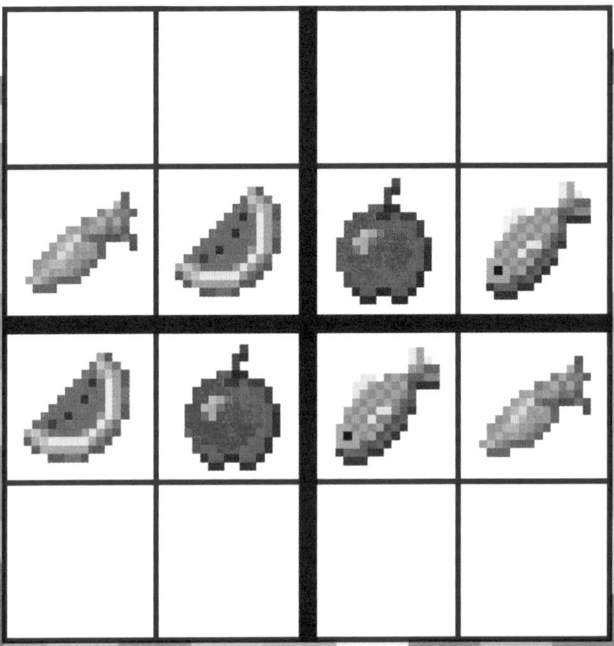

FIND THE WORD

THIS 3X3 block of letters is hiding a **Minecraft item** that is very useful for **sending things sky-high**. Choose a starting letter then see if you can trace your way around the block – up, down, left or right – to find the hidden word.

R	P	N
E	O	U
D	W	G

10 MINUTES!

YOU'LL NEVER PUT ME OUT WITH YOUR PUNY HOSEPIPES!

FIRE ENGINE

Using 999 blocks (not really!)

DIFFICULTY

EASY
A SIMPLE BUILD FOR THOSE JUST STARTING OUT IN MINECRAFT

START HERE!

1 THE BASE of your engine is a 4x10 rectangle of **Stone Slabs**, with **Black Wool** wheels inserted, as above. Put **Buttons** on the wheels. On top of this build a **Red Clay** cab – 4 blocks at the front, 3 down the side, 2 up with **Black Stained Glass** panes to fill in the windscreen.

2 ABOVE THE windscreen use **Quartz, Quartz Stairs** and **Quartz Slabs** to finish the roof. Add an **Iron Door** on both sides. For the body, copy the pattern above in **Red Stained Clay** 2 blocks high, then repeat again with **Quartz**, except for 2 blocks at the back of your engine.

3 ADD DETAIL around your Fire Engine – the gaps in the side should be filled with **Quartz Stairs**, and again on the back of the Engine. Now you need a ladder on the roof – we built ours from **4 Wooden Stairs**, **4 blocks of Polished Andesite** and **10 Stone Slabs** – finishing above the front.

4 THERE ARE lots of cool things you can now add to your Fire Engine to decorate it – **Ladders** on the sides, **Item Frames** with coloured **Wool** inside for lights – we have red above the cab, white on the front and orange on the sides. More **Ladders** on the front and for a number plate! A **Lever** next to the **Door** will open it up... cool!

BUILD THIS!

KNOW YOUR BIOMES
OCEAN

WOULD YOU BELIEVE that over 60% of the Overworld's surface is made up of Ocean biome? That's almost as much as our own Earth at 70%! An Ocean biome is basically made of Water blocks, stretching out as far as you can see, usually 3,000 blocks on one direction. You can find islands floating in the Ocean if you go exploring, but stock up on food first!

THE ONE MOB THAT YOU WILL FIND IN GREAT SUPPLY IN THE OCEAN IS THE SQUID. THESE EIGHT-ARMED MOBS SPAWN IN WATER YOU SEE. THEY WON'T DO YOU ANY HARM.

THERE IS ANOTHER BIOME CALLED DEEP OCEAN THAT IS WELL WORTH CHECKING OUT AS THIS IS WHERE OCEAN MONUMENTS CAN FORM, AND THIS IS WHERE YOU WILL FIND GUARDIANS, SPONGE AND PRISMARINE BLOCKS.

ROCK AROUND THE BLOCK!

WHAT IS STEVE'S FAVOURITE SONG?

MINECRAFT
TIPS CARDS!
CUT OUT AND KEEP EXPERT TIPS CARDS

ARMOUR Chain Helmet

IF YOU want to protect your head then luckily there are five types of **Helmet** in Minecraft. This Chain Helmet isn't the **strongest**, but will increase your **Defense points by 2**. It also looks great on!

UTILITY Bed

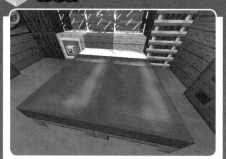

THE bed is actually just **1 block**, and when used to go to sleep it will **reset your spawn point** to nearby. Beds come in a multitude of colours and can be Crafted using **3 matching Wool** blocks and **3 Wood Planks** of any type.

DECOR Item Frame

YOU'VE seen those 'Break glass in case of emergency' signs, right? Well this is Minecraft's equivalent. You can put any item inside an **Item Frame**, then when you need it just **punch the frame** and it will drop out!

DECOR Zombie Head

IF a nasty mob gets blown up in a **Charged Creeper explosion** they will drop their head! You can then pick up the head and wear it as a **disguise!** Above we're wearing a Zombie Head, great for sneaking through Zombies!

ARMOUR Diamond Leggings

IF it's your legs you want to protect then you're going to need some **armoured Leggings**. The toughest you can find in the game are the **Diamond Leggings**. Much better than the flimsy Leather Pants!

UTILITY Saddle

YOU want to go for a ride on a mob in Minecraft? You're going to need to place a **Saddle** on them first! You can **Trade** one from **Leatherworker Villagers for 8-10 Emeralds**, or find one on your travels.

MINECRAFT TIPS CARDS!

GRRR... ALL THESE CARDS AND NO SIGN OF CREEPERS!

▶ BECOME A MINECRAFT EXPERT!

THESE SPECIAL Limited Edition Minecraft tips cards have been created by our expert Minecrafters for you. Covering Blocks, Items, Mobs, Weapons, Food, Vehicles and more! All you need to do is cut them out by carefully cutting along the dotted lines (round off the corners if you like). Then keep them handy the next time you play!

MINECRAFT TIPS CARDS!
GAMES MASTER PRESENTS

Item Frame

- CRAFTING an Item Frame can be done by combining 8 Sticks and 1 Leather together.
- THERE is only one naturally generating Item Frame in the game – on an End Ship containing Elytra.
- PLACE a Map inside an Item Frame and the Map will enlarge to show your location with a green pointer.
- THE Achievement 'Map Room' can be earned by placing 9 Maps in Item Frames in a 3x3 square.

MINECRAFT TIPS CARDS!
GAMES MASTER PRESENTS

Bed

- YOU don't always have to Craft your bed, they do naturally generate in the world too – inside Igloos in the icy biomes.
- GO to sleep in a Bed by pressing the Use button. You can only sleep at night-time though, unless there's a thunderstorm going on!
- BEFORE you face The End or The Nether, get plenty of sleep. Placing a Bed there will make it explode if you try to sleep in it!

MINECRAFT TIPS CARDS!
GAMES MASTER PRESENTS

Chain Helmet

- THERE are five types of Helmet in the game: Leather Cap, Chain Helmet, Iron, Diamond & Gold.
- IF you have two Helmets that are damaged, you can Craft them both together to create one good one.
- BADLY damaged Helmets can often be picked up from defeated mobs like Zombies or Skeletons in armour.
- YOU can use Enchantments on Helmets to increase their usefulness in battles.

MINECRAFT TIPS CARDS!
GAMES MASTER PRESENTS

Saddle

- SADDLES are found in Chests in varying numbers. Nether Fortresses have the most, followed by Desert Temples and Dungeons.
- THE other way you can find a Saddle is through Fishing! Occasionally you'll hook one instead of a fish!
- PIGS, Mules, Donkeys and Horses can have a Saddle used on them to make them controllable when you ride. To control a Pig you will also need a Carrot on a Stick!

MINECRAFT TIPS CARDS!
GAMES MASTER PRESENTS

Diamond Leggings

- SEVEN Diamonds can be Crafted together to make yourself a pair of Diamond Leggings.
- THERE is a slim chance that Skeletons, Zombie Pigmen or Zombies will drop Leggings on death.
- PLACE armoured Leggings in the third armour slot in your inventory to use them.
- DIAMOND Leggings are very durable with a value of 496, compared to 76 for Leather ones.

MINECRAFT TIPS CARDS!
GAMES MASTER PRESENTS

Zombie Head

- WEARING a Zombie Head is a great way to break the ice at a party, but it does have a useful purpose too...
- YOU can sneak through a pack of Zombies in disguise with one of these on your head! They are 50% less likely to spot you.
- THEY can also be used in Crafting. Combine a Zombie Head with Gunpowder and any Dye to make a Firework that explodes in the shape of a Creeper – cool!

FOOD Cookie

COME on, you don't need a reason to want a Cookie, do you? They are a very common food in **Minecraft**, even though they do not actually give you much energy. But if you do find some **Cocoa Beans**, give them a try!

ITEM Bottle o'Enchanting

EVERYBODY knows how crucial **Experience Orbs** are to getting anywhere in **Minecraft**, and you can get them in loads of ways – but using the **Bottle o'Enchanting** has to be the coolest – just throw it, and generate orbs!

TOOL Wooden Hoe

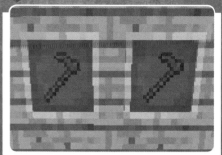

SHOULD you wish to till **Dirt** and **Grass Blocks** into **Farmland Blocks**, you're going to need this trusty tool by your side. There are four other kinds of Hoe, though: **Stone, Iron, Golden and Diamond Hoes**. Very posh!

ARMOUR Iron Chestplate

PROTECTING your **upper body**, the **Iron Chestplate** is stronger than Gold, Leather or Chainmail, but not as strong as Diamond. A **Blacksmith** will sell you one for **10-14 Emeralds**. Craft one with **8 Iron Ingots**.

UTILITY Brewing Stand

MAKING up a single block, a **Brewing Stand** is used for brewing **Potions, Splash Potions and Lingering Potions**. They can be Crafted combining a **Blaze Rod** and 3 blocks of **Cobblestone** together.

DECOR Music Disc

MINECRAFT has its own built-in music to enjoy. Using a **Jukebox** you can play these **Music Discs**, seen here in an Item Frame. There are **12 tunes** in total, created by **Daniel Rosenfeld**, otherwise known as C418.

DECOR Painting

THEY may be only a **decorative item**, but you can use Paintings in a variety of ways to make your builds look more realistic. For example, use one on a block to make it look like a **computer monitor**!

ARMOUR Horse Armour

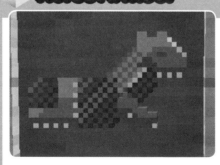

PROTECTING your horse is important! You need some Horse Armour for it to wear, it is found in **Chests** in the Overworld and The End in varying amounts. It comes in **Leather, Iron, Gold** and **Diamond** variations.

UTILITY Armour Stand

WANT to show off your best armour? Then you need an Armour Stand! They are crafted from **6 Sticks** and a **Stone Slab**, but be careful when swinging your Sword around one – **2 hits** and it will break!

Games Master Presents

MINECRAFT TIPS CARDS!

Wooden Hoe

YOU can find Wooden Hoes just through exploring and mining, but it takes more ingredients to forge the other kinds of Hoe.

THE most simple kind of Hoe, it has 1 Attack Speed and 1 Attack Damage when equipped, so don't expect to win many battles with one!

THE Wooden Hoe has 60 uses to the Stone Hoe's 132, but you've got to eat, so you have to start your farming career somewhere.

Games Master Presents

MINECRAFT TIPS CARDS!

Bottle o'Enchanting

ONE way to get your hands on one is by bartering with a Village Cleric – they will let you have one for 3-11 Emeralds, as a fourth tier trade.

THEY are easy enough to use – you just press 'Use'! The Experience Orbs they produce should be worth 3-11 Experience Points.

YOU cannot actually craft any of these potions, but in Survival Mode they do become available via trading with villagers.

Games Master Presents

MINECRAFT TIPS CARDS!

Cookie

BAKING Cookies is a fine art in real life, but all you need to craft them is 2 Wheat, 1 Cocoa Beans and that will get you 8 Cookies all at once – handy for small energy boosts.

ON the other hand, Villager Farmers will trade 6–10 Cookies for 1 Emerald as a fourth tier trade.

DON'T ever give a Cookie to a Parrot! Not only will the Parrot die, it will emit Poison Particles in its death throes! Poor polly!

Games Master Presents

MINECRAFT TIPS CARDS!

Music Disc

WHILE there are 12 default Music Discs in the game, these can be changed using Resource Packs.

IF you kill a Creeper with a Skeleton's Arrow it will drop a random Music Disc.

THE 12 Music Discs have titles like 'Blocks', 'Mellohi', 'Strad' and 'Cat'. They are a mix of musical styles.

PLAYING your first Music Disc in the console game will earn you the 'Music To My Ears' Achievement.

Games Master Presents

MINECRAFT TIPS CARDS!

Brewing Stand

YOU can find naturally generating Brewing Stands in End City ships, the basement of Igloos and sometimes in Witch's Huts found in Swampland biomes.

PRESS Use on a Brewing Stand to start it, it is fuelled by Blaze Powder, 1 piece gives 20 attempts at brewing.

TO brew yourself a Potion you need to combine the ingredients, Blaze Powder and a Bottle.

Games Master Presents

MINECRAFT TIPS CARDS!

Iron Chestplate

YOU can double the durability of damaged matching Chestplates by Crafting them together, you even get a bonus 5% durability on top.

OVER a quarter of all Blacksmiths chests will have an Iron Chestplate inside them. 12% of Stronghold altar chests will also have one.

YOU activate a Chestplate by placing it in the second armour slot in your inventory. An Iron Chestplate will take 241 damage.

Games Master Presents

MINECRAFT TIPS CARDS!

Armour Stand

THESE things are very versatile – they can hold armour, but also mob heads, pumpkins or dispensers.

TO store your armour just use it on the stand and it will appear on it. Click it again to put it back on.

YOU can customise Armour Stands to give them arms, float and pose in various ways using NBT Tags.

WHEN placing an Armour Stand you can choose which orientation you prefer, a bit like Signs or Banners.

Games Master Presents

MINECRAFT TIPS CARDS!

Horse Armour

IF you are struggling to find Horse Armour in Pocket Edition Chests you can Craft some for yourself with 7 Leather.

LEATHER Horse Armour only gives 3 defense points, Iron gives 5, Gold 7 and Diamond 11.

HAS your horse run away so you no longer need its Iron or Gold armour? Well you can Smelt it down by Crafting it with any fuel. It will turn back into its original metal.

Games Master Presents

MINECRAFT TIPS CARDS!

Painting

CRAFT a Painting using 8 Sticks with any colour of Wool. The colour doesn't affect anything.

WHEN placed, a Painting will check what space it has on the wall and give you a random sized Painting. To restrict its size, give it less space!

THE game has 26 Paintings in it that appear at random. Most are based on original paintings by Swedish artist Kristoffer Zetterstrand.

RAW — Popped Chorus Fruit

NOWHERE does Minecraft get weirder than with the Chorus Fruit. Their teleportation properties are odd enough, but if you smelt them, you get Popped Chorus Fruit – no longer edible, but ready to make Purpur Blocks.

PLANT — Wheat

PROBABLY one of the most versatile items you can find, Wheat can be baked into Bread or Cake, it can be used to lure animals, or even get them to breed, plus it can be traded for loads of things. Everyone wants Wheat!

ITEM — Blaze Powder

BLAZE Powder is a very potent Brewing ingredient, and has a whole host of uses for you to master. It all starts when you get a Blaze Rod from the Blaze – the tricksy flaming mob that spawns in the Nether Fortresses.

FOOD — Cake

YOU can eat Cake! (Obviously) but once Cake is placed anywhere, it cannot be recollected even with the use of Silk touch. You can make a Cake block using the ingredients Milk, Sugar, Egg and Wheat. Just like in real life!

UTILITY — Enchanted Book

PLACING enchantments on certain objects can have mind-blowing results. Enchanted Books are what you need to achieve this, and they can be found in Chests randomly littered about, or even found by fishing.

DECOR — Flower Pot

THESE decorative items seem straightforward – they can be mined with or without a tool, and will drop as an item when pushed by a Piston. Also look out for them in Witch Huts on your travels.

RAW — Leather

MAKING armour is a craft that takes some practice, but Leather Armour is worth looking into. Cows, Mooshrooms, Horses and Llamas drop up to two pieces of Leather when they die. Do not let them die in vain!

BLOCK — Lava

LAVA can be a very dangerous material, and will hurt you! It is a light-emitting fluid block with many uses. It can cause fires by turning air blocks into fire blocks. A single block can also cause a flow of lava, of 3 blocks.

UTILITY — Sign

THESE are non-solid blocks used for displaying text. They can be made with or without a tool, but using an Axe will get fastest results. Don't forget you'll also need to have a Stick to craft one!

MINECRAFT TIPS CARDS!

Blaze Powder

- ONCE you have managed to get a Blaze Rod from one of the Blaze Mobs you can extract the Blaze Powder!

- ADD your Powder to an Ender Pearl to craft the Eye of Ender, to a Slimeball to craft Magma Cream, or just combine with Coal & Gunpowder for explosive Fire Charges!

- FOR brewing, one of these is all you need for a Mundane Potion, or add an Awkward Potion for a Potion of Strength!

MINECRAFT TIPS CARDS!

Wheat

- IN Minecraft cookery, Wheat is the only item you need – 3, to be precise – to make Bread. For Cake you will need Egg, Sugar and Milk, or 2 Wheat 1 Cocoa Beans will get a Cookie.

- HORSES also love Wheat, and 1 Wheat will heal a horse 1 unit, or it can lower its temper by 3% when you're taming it.

- IF you herd together two cows, sheep, or mooshrooms, using Wheat on them triggers Love Mode!

MINECRAFT TIPS CARDS!

Popped Chorus Fruit

- WHEN you get Chorus Fruit from the Chorus Plant, you just need to add any fuel to turn it into the no-longer-edible Popped variety!

- YOU will need 4 Popped Chorus Fruit in order to craft Purpur Blocks in The End.

- YOU can also craft an End Rod by combining your Popped Chorus Fruit with a Blaze Rod.

MINECRAFT TIPS CARDS!

Flower Pot

- NEED somewhere to put a plant? Plants that can be placed in Flower Pots include 1 block high Flowers, Saplings, Ferns, Dead Bushes, Mushrooms and Cacti.

- FLOWER Pots can also be used to step on, and to jump up to higher areas, such as Fences.

- WHEN a cactus is placed in a Flower Pot it will no longer harm you. Also, they will break falling Sand and Gravel blocks.

MINECRAFT TIPS CARDS!

Enchanted Book

- BESIDES exploring all the Chests and fishing for Books, they can also be obtained via Trading, or you can just enchant a normal Book if placed on an Enchantment Table.

- USING Enchanted Books is not easy. You have to place it in an Anvil with the item you wish to enchant. You'll need plenty of experience too!

- JUST like weapons and tools, Enchanted Books can be combined to make a stronger single Book.

MINECRAFT TIPS CARDS!

Cake

- FARMER Villagers sell 1 Cake for 1 Emerald as a fourth tier trade. That's one expensive Cake!

- YOU cannot just eat a Cake right out of your hotbar. You first have to place it on a block – Cakes have 7 slices to enjoy once you do get stuck in!

- CAKE can actually destroy falling blocks if placed under them, like a Torch. You can even make a Staircase out of them! Yum!

MINECRAFT TIPS CARDS!

Sign

- YOU can place a Sign on the top or side of other blocks (including non-solid blocks like Fences, Glass, Rails, and even other Signs!

- SIGNS are there to display text – and you can fit up to 4 lines of text on any given sign.

- THERE are many other uses for Signs such as burning them for fuel! Though they are not burned by Lava. You can also block a Piston from moving with one.

MINECRAFT TIPS CARDS!

Lava

- LAVA cannot just be picked up, you have to use a special Bucket to draw it. Don't try this in real life!

- WATER and Lava can produce Stone, Cobblestone or Obsidian, depending on how they interact.

- WHEN lava is flowing, it will destroy many things in its path, including Saplings, Cobweb, Tall Grass, Dead Bush, Wheat, Flowers, Mushrooms, Lily Pads, Vines, Levers, Buttons, Torches, Redstone and more.

MINECRAFT TIPS CARDS!

Leather

- YOU can sometimes get hold of some handy Leather without much effort – it can be found as junk when fishing, if you're lucky.

- ITEMS which can be crafted from Leather include Books, Frames, Boots, Caps, Armour, Pants and Tunics. Leather pants? Yikes.

- LEATHERWORKER Villagers will buy 9-12 leather for an Emerald. Also, you can mend any Leather item by using an Anvil.

FOOD | Milk

YOU can get yourself a bucket of milk from a Cow or Mooshroom by simply standing next to them with an empty bucket and tapping Use. Press Use again once the bucket is full and you will drink heartily from the Milk!

ITEM | Ghast Tear

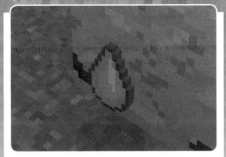

WHEN you kill a Ghast, they will drop a Ghast Tear, which is bound to make you feel a bit sorry for them! These Tears should be collected up as they are very useful in crafting recipes to make weird and wonderful stuff.

MOB | Agent

YOU won't find Agent hanging out in the regular Minecraft game. To find him you need to download Minecraft: Education Edition. He's there to help people learn coding using Minecraft – great fun!

FOOD | Beetroot Soup

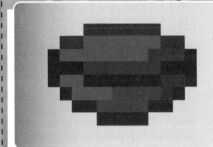

THIS may come as a major surprise, but you can craft Beetroot Soup from one key ingredient – Beetroot. You will need 6 of them to be precise, plus a Bowl, and eating it restores 6 health and 7.2 saturation.

UTILITY | Carrot on a stick

CARROTS on sticks have long been seen as ways of getting what you want, but in Minecraft, they have one use only – making sure Pigs go exactly where you want them when you're riding them. Pigs love carrots.

DECOR | Mob Head

WHAT do you have in common with a building? Well, you can both decorate yourself with a Mob Head – either wearing it as a mask, or popping one on a structure as a decorative touch. They can be used as disguises, too.

RAW | Redstone

REDSTONE is a flat transparent block transmitting Redstone Power – bringing all sorts of mechanisms to life. Among many ways of obtaining it, you can craft Redstone from Redstone Blocks and smelt it from Redstone Ore.

BLOCK | Fire

SURELY you know what Fire is – it's the really hot orange stuff you shouldn't touch! And in Minecraft it is a dangerous but crucial substance, which can burn its way through many flammable blocks – help and hindrance.

UTILITY | Totem of Undying

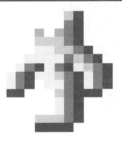

EVERYONE should get hold of this magical doohickey, as it can save you from death – and who doesn't want saving from death occasionally? But you will not have one until you have bested an Evoker in battle.

MINECRAFT TIPS CARDS!

Agent

SCRATCHX is the interface used in **Education Edition** for Agent to help teach coding to Minecraft fans, through **Code Connection for Minecraft**.

THERE is an inventory of 27 items that Agent can carry that are then programmed using commands or the in-game user interface.

CODING noobs can quickly pick up the basics of programming by dragging and dropping commands to Agent in the visual interface. It's fun!

MINECRAFT TIPS CARDS!

Ghast Tear

YOU can craft yourself an **End Crystal** using a Ghast's Tear. You need to mix it with **Glass** and **Eye of Ender**, which will save you searching for one in The End.

GHAST Tears can also be used as brewing ingredients. A **Mundane Potion** can be acheived using a Ghast Tear and a **Water Bottle**. While **Potion of Regeneration** is made using an **Awkward Potion** along with a Ghast's Tear. Useful, eh?

MINECRAFT TIPS CARDS!

Milk

DRINKING Milk will remove all status effects from you. Drink while in first-person mode and you will see an animation of you drinking!

MILK is really useful to use in recipes to make other stuff in Minecraft. Try adding it to **Sugar**, **Wheat** and **Egg** to make a **Cake**!

THERE'S even an achievement you can received called 'The Lie' that you earn by learning to bake a cake using Milk as one of the ingredients.

MINECRAFT TIPS CARDS!

Mob Head

MOB Heads can be broken using anything, and will drop itself when broken. If a player head has a custom skin, it'll stay when broken.

IF a Mob Head is pushed by a **Piston**, or if one comes in contact with **Water** or **Lava**, it will also break off as an item.

YOU can wear heads, similarly to **Pumpkins** or **Helmets**. This will overlay the second layer of your character's skin. Yikes!

MINECRAFT TIPS CARDS!

Carrot on a Stick

WHEREAS you cannot make soup from a carrot in Minecraft, you can use one to **control Pigs** as you ride them around. Here's how to make one...

YOU will need a **Carrot**, obviously, and also a **Fishing Rod** and a **Crafting Table**. Always put the Carrot in the centre square, the Rod in the first.

ONCE you have made your Pig bait, jump on and get exploring! But whatever you do, do not attempt this in real life. Pigs really hate it.

MINECRAFT TIPS CARDS!

Beetroot Soup

SOUP should be an obvious option when **crafting meals** out of the raw ingredients you find as you explore. And yet only Beetroot Soup is available!

THE closest the game otherwise gets to soup, is your ability to prepare **Mushroom Stew** and **Rabbit Stew**. Minecraft needs more recipes!

BESIDES of course a generous amount of beetroots, to make soup you will always need a **bowl** in your inventory. Or you will get messy.

MINECRAFT TIPS CARDS!

Totem of Undying

EVOKERS are obviously horrible chaps to come up against, but at least you know **if you beat them in battle** one of these Totems will be yours.

IF you are holding one of these in either your main or off-hand slots, and receive otherwise **fatal damage**, it will prevent you from dying.

ALTHOUGH handy, these Totems will not save you from death caused by the **/kill** command, or void damage. So remain on your guard!

MINECRAFT TIPS CARDS!

Fire

FIRE can be placed using **Flint** and **Steel** or a **Fire Charge**. It will spread across flammable blocks, and can spontaneously ignite when flammable blocks are near **Lava**, so watch out.

THERE are other ways fire will start and spread – a **Lightning Bolt** can cause fires, while they start naturally in **The Nether**.

WORRIED everything's going to burn down? **Fire** will stop when it reaches non-flammable blocks.

MINECRAFT TIPS CARDS!

Redstone

HOW to get it? Try mining or smelting **Redstone Ore**, destroying jungle temple traps, killing **Witches**, trading with **Villagers**, and more!

YOU can break **Redstone Dust** with or without a tool; it drops itself as an item, so there's one more way.

WITCHES have good sides – a single witch will drop 0 to 6 Redstone when they die, even if you're not the one who killed them. With the **Looting** enchantment, even more!

Make it!
PIG OPEN SANDWICH!

Oink! Let us show you how to make a Minecraft Pig sandwich. Mmmm... pig.

1 SQUARE EYES

MOBS MAY come and mobs may go, but the favourite Minecraft mob for Team Mayhem will always be the pig! They're just so darn cute... and so tasty too! So for our last Make It feature we're turning our faves into open sandwiches. You will need square bread, sliced ham, sliced cheese and chorizo, plus tomato sauce if you like it. Start by spreading sauce over your bread for some 'glue'! Now place a square of ham on your bread. Make some ham 'pixels' to place on top of it to give it that Minecraft look. Faces are 8x8 pixels, but these are too small, so we say cut your pixel squares to around 2cm in size. Then 2 strips of cheese for the base of the nose.

2 PORKY PIXELS

NOW OPEN up the chorizo and cut yourself four 'pixels' of the darker coloured piggy goodness. Place 2 either side of the nose, and two where your pig's eyes are going to be. Put a single ham 'pixel' in the centre of the nose and then add two cheese 'pixels' on the inside of the eyes to make up the square look of the eyeballs. Look at our handiwork here for the correct placement of all the pieces. You remember what a Minecraft pig looks like, right?

3 TOASTY GOODNESS!

YOU CAN either eat your Pig Open Sandwich cold (yeuck!) or pop it under the grill for about 5 minutes until the cheese melts and the chorizo goes all crispy around the edges. The sauce will warm through and bread toast around the edges too, giving you one delicious Minecraft Pig Open Sandwich that tastes like the most yummy pizza you ever had! Now scoff it.

20 MINUTES!

WHERE IS THE
SECRET ENTRANCE?
IF I TOLD YOU, IT WOULDN'T
BE SECRET!

A SECRET WALL

A secret wall entrance may come in very handy!

DIFFICULTY

NORMAL
QUITE A SIMPLE BUILD, BUT
MAY BE VERY USEFUL...

START HERE!

1 **FIRST THINGS** first, pull out some Stone and Sticky Pistons. Lay down six Stone blocks all in a long row and knock out the middle two blocks. Next, on the left side, create an 'L' shape out of Sticky Pistons. After that, head to the right and do the same but in reverse.

2 **PLACE YOUR** wall blocks in front of the Sticky Pistons. We're using Gold blocks here to show you where they should go, but If your wall is going to be made of Stone, use Stone blocks instead. After that, run a row of Stone blocks across the top-front to create an archway.

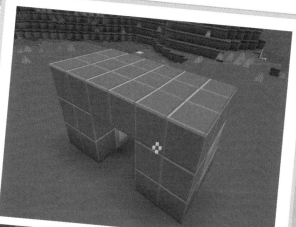

3 **THE NEXT** thing we need to do is build a roof on top of our device so we can lay down Redstone. Coming from the row above the doorframe, add in another 2 rows behind it. You can now go ahead and add Redstone Repeaters and Redstone Dust to your hotbar.

4 **ONE BLOCK** in from both sides place down Redstone Repeaters facing outward. This next part is important: Hit each of them once so they're both on 2 ticks. If you don't, the wall will push the wrong parts out. Next dust in the Redstone in between and around, as shown.

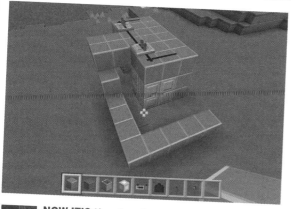

5 NOW IT'S time to add in somewhere for our *Lever* to go. Add in 4 blocks behind the *Redstone Dust*. Next add a *Step* down, build it 4 blocks out, then 4 to the right. Do not build the arm too close to the Pistons as it'll accidentally activate them, and we really don't want that.

6 LOOKING FROM the back, connect the *Redstone Dust* on the right (in between the *Repeaters*) down and along the stone arm. One block after the steps, drop in a *Repeater* facing the steps. At the end of the arm add another block with a *Lever* on its face.

7 GO ON. You know you want to. Pull the *Lever* and marvel at our really simple, really compact, Redstone secret wall. If you're looking to add a *Lever* on the inside, place one on the back of the step you made leading to the lever. That way you can close the wall behind you.

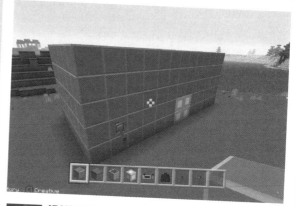

8 IF YOU'RE creating this out in the open, now's a good time to build up the walls around it. Do keep in mind you don't want to place blocks directly on top of the Redstone as it will *disrupt the circuit*. So be sure to build the walls a few blocks taller to avoid any issues.

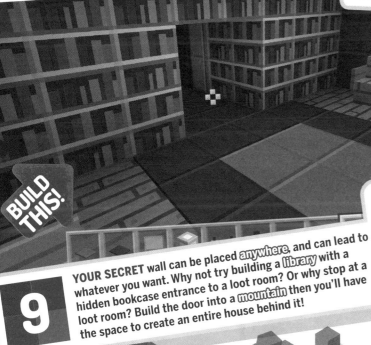

BUILD THIS!

9 YOUR SECRET wall can be placed *anywhere*, and can lead to whatever you want. Why not try building a *library* with a hidden bookcase entrance to a loot room? Or why stop at a loot room? Build the door into a *mountain* then you'll have the space to create an entire house behind it!

I READ A BOOK ONCE. GREEN, IT WAS.

PUZZLE ANSWERS

Try solving them yourself first – no cheating!

PAGE 10-11

LEAFY MAZE

FIND THE WORD
It was FERMENTED.

NAME THAT MOB
1. Shulker, 2. Ocelot, 3. Snow Golem.

LIGHTNING CODE
The hidden phrase was THE ENDER DRAGON IS CHARGING.

PAGE 29

TRACKBLOCK
Minecraft, Flowerpot, Bookshelf

HIDDEN BLOCKS
Grass, Melon, Slime, Magma

QUACK!

SPOT THE DIFFERENCE

PAGE 34

NAME THAT MOB
1. Pig, 2. Enderman, 3. Guardian, 4. Llama, 5. Blaze, 6. Zombie, 7. Mooshroom.

FIND THE WORD
It was GUNPOWDER.

FOOD SUDOKU

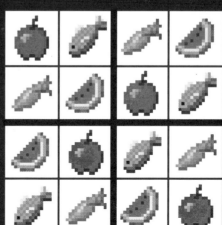